THE VINTAGE MAD

Edited by

Albert B. Feldstein

WARNER BOOKS

A Warner Communications Company

"The times . . . they are a-changing!" sang *Bobby Dylan. Well, nowhere have the times a-changed things as dramatically as they have on the American College Campus. To illustrate these vast changes, we'd like to present excerpts from two College Yearbooks . . . one, a typical Yearbook from your parents' college generation, and the other, a typical Yearbook of today. Here, then, is . . .*

A MAD LOOK AT TWO COLLEGE GENERA- TIONS

ARTIST: GEORGE WOODBRIDGE

WRITER: LARRY SIEGEL

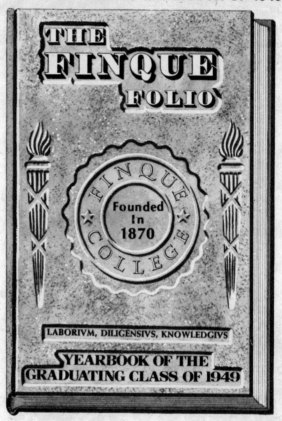

THE
FINQUE
FOLIO

FINQUE

Founded
In
1870

COLLEGE

LABORIVM, DILIGENSIVS, KNOWLEDGIVS

YEARBOOK OF THE
GRADUATING CLASS OF 1949

THE CLASS OF 1949

HOWARD J. WHITNEY
HomeTown: Akron, Ohio

Treasurer of the Library Club, Organizer of the Zeta Beta Psi Sunday School Picnics, President of the Kay Kayser Campus Fan Club.

Math Medal, ROTC Good Conduct Medal.

Voted: Boy Most Likely To Be An Accountant.

Ambition: *"To become a CPA, marry the girl next door, have three children, and be the best jitterbug in Akron, Ohio."*

LINDA FERNSCHREIBER
HomeTown: Merrick, Long Island

Home Economics Major, Vice President of the Senior Girls Hygiene and Moral Cleanliness Club, Chairman of the Campus Beautification Committee, Junior Class Dating Chaperon, Campus Representative for B'nai B'rith.

Ambition: *"To get married, move into a Mother-Daughter Two-Family House (with my husband downstairs, and my mother and I upstairs) and become the Mah Jong Champion of all Nassau County."*

WASHINGTON LINCOLN JONES
HomeTown: Savannah, Georgia

President of the Senior Boys Tap Dancing Club, Secretary of the Stepin Fetchit Fan Club, Captain of the Union Building Shoe-Shine Team, Vice-President of the Cafeteria Kitchen Squad.

Merit Award for Creative Chicken-Frying.

Voted: Boy most likely to be a Bell Hop.

Ambition: *"To be the best (and only) Bell Hop ever to graduate from college."*

THE CLASS OF 1969

FRIG STUYVESANT
HomeTown: Freakout, Maine

Senior Class Travel Agent for LSD Trips, Campus Representative of Mao Tse Tung, Dean's Office Wrecking Squad, Captain of the Dow Chemical Campus Baiting Society.

Picketing and Protesting Honor Roll.

Voted: Most Conscientious Campus Conscientious Objector

Ambition: *"After 4 years as an outstanding campus agitator at Finque I hope someday to enroll in this school as a student."*

FLEUR VERBANICK
HomeTown: Detroit, Michigan

Treasurer of the Senior Latin-American Revolutionary Council, Senior Girls Pot Monitor, Campus Liason for Imprisoned Student Demonstrators, Chairman of the Free Love Society, Captain of the Union Building Window-Smashing Squad.

Voted:
Unmarried Campus Mother-Of-The-Year.

Ambition: *"To run away and live in a cave with Ho Chi Minh.*

RAP WHITE
HomeTown: Greenwich Village, N.Y.

Captain of the Student Store Looting Team, President of the Sidney Poitier Movie Campus Picketing Squad, All-Star Campus Soul Brother, Senior Class Black Panther Honkey Chasing Committee.

Voted: Boy least likely to be called "Boy"

Ambition: *"I want everything, Man! Not now! YESTERDAY!!"*

1949 CANDID CAMPUS PHOTOS

CAMPUS LOVE

The hottest (Wow!) spot on campus is Sin Alley, outside the Women's Residence Hall. Here's a shot of a typical bunch of students engaged in all kinds of wild sex like hugging, ear-blowing and heavy handshaking. Hubba-hubba!

A TYPICAL CLASS

Thirty-three Finque students attend typical Lecture class in Pfeffer Hall. Note madcap student at left swallowing a goldfish. Ain't we the craziest generation? Solid, Jackson!

PEP RALLY

Finque students build huge bonfire of boxes and crates in order to encourage football team for big game with State. Note close likeness of State coach Pop Gribbish, who is being hanged in effigy. Go, team, go! Hey-bob-a-ree-bob!

1969 CANDID CAMPUS PHOTOS

CAMPUS LOVE

Only a generation ago, square Finque students would hang around Sin Alley behind the Women's Residence Hall and engage in silly necking. Today, as you can see by this photo, the Women's Residence Hall is a serious Family Center where students of all sexes live together and raise children together and sometimes even get married.

A TYPICAL CLASS

Thirty-three thousand Finque students attend typical class in Pfeffer Football Stadium. This is a Discussion group. Lecture groups meet Tuesdays and Fridays in Grand Canyon.

PEP RALLY

Finque students build huge bonfire of Chemistry building and Gym in order to encourage Board of Trustees to banish military recruiters from the campus. Note close likeness of Army Recruiting Sgt. Buck Chicken, who is being hanged in effigy. Hey, come to think of it, that *is* Sgt. Chicken!

1949 CAMPUS FRATERNITIES

Here's that swell bunch of guys at Sigma Dela Wasp, the most restricted White Protestant fraternity on campus. Seated (left to right): Arnold Pure, Daniel White, William Anglo and Thomas Saxon. Standing (left to right): Pure Waverly, White Lockhart, Anglo McKeesick and Saxon American. Standing (far off to the side of the group): Robert Edward Bigot, a pushy Presbyterian.

This is that real great group of guys at Alpha Beta Sig. All of us on campus are proud of them. They never cause trouble, they're very polite, and they know their place, mainly six miles off campus. Standing (left to right): Leroy, James, Willie, Amos and Andy. Seated (left to right): Jackson, Birmingham, Alabama, Lightnin' and Sam.

1969 CAMPUS FRATERNITIES

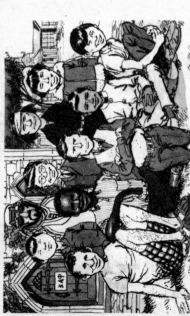

Here is Sigma Delta Wasp, once the most bigoted White Protestant fraternity on campus. But we got after those Neanderthal creeps and changed all that. Now, it's open to everyone, regardless of race, color, or nationality. Seated (l. to r.): Murray Bernstein, Homer Jones, Spyros Kouris, Nehru Pandit and Lou Fong. Standing (l. to r.) Kim Korea, Ahmed Hussar, Haya Kido, Joe Thundercloud, and Nanook Nome. (Not in picture: Vito Pizzeria, Pedro Gonzales and Honorary Brother—Viet Cong Divinity Student Ngh Chu Hinh.)

Once a segregated Negro ghetto fraternity set up by the White Campus Establishment, Alpha Beta Sig is now almost completely integrated . . . with White Protestants. Seated (left to right): Arnold Pure, Jr., Daniel White, Jr., William Anglo, Jr. and Thomas Saxon, Jr. Standing (left to right) Pure Waverly, Jr., White Lockhart, Jr., Anglo McKeesick, Jr., Saxon American, Jr. and Stokely Brown.

1949 CLASS FAREWELLS

ALMA MATER

By Herbert Flotts
President of
the Senior Class

The campus grass is green and verdant
  As the sun begins to sink;
With heavy heart and laden step I
  Say farewell to dear old Finque.
I'll miss your ivy-covered buildings
  And your profs who made me think;
And though a wond'rous world awaits me,
  I will not forget you, Finque.
Should someone from another college
  Ever join me for a drink
And boast of his dear Alma Mater,
  I'll not flinch and I'll not blink;
I'll stare him down and say quite proudly:
"You're a Harvard . . . ?
I'M A FINQUE!"

A Message From
Dr. Hutchinson R. Kinkaid
President of Finque College

To the Class of 1949:

Your years at Finque College will soon be over.
And they were four wonderful years, I am sure.
But you must not look backward at the years
behind you. You must look forward to the years
ahead of you. For to go backward at a time in
your life when you should be going forward is
like starting a book at its end and reading
toward its beginning which, in essence, has
already begun long before you end it.

And so, just as you cannot begin a book at
its end and end it at its beginning, so you
must begin your life at its beginning and
end your life at its end (and vice versa for
all you Israeli Exchange Students!).
Good luck and God bless you all.

1969 CLASS FAREWELLS

ALMA MATER

By Ravi Ravnick
Chairman of the Students
of the New Left

Finque, Finque, Finque,
You quagmire of stultified
Establishmentarianism
Whose grasses were polluted
By the blood-stained boots of the fuzz
When they crushed my fragile body
But spared my brain
So that it could be numbed by
Chaucer and Donne and Darwin
When my heart cried out for Che!
Finque, Finque, Finque,
You offer me a diploma,
A scrolled symbol of oppression,
Printed by the very same men
Whose money-hungry hands
Also printed my Draft Card
On the vile paper processed from trees
Destroyed to make room for super-highways
That led Reagan to Sacramento
And Nixon to Washington?
Well,
shove
it,
Alma
Mater!

A Message From
Dr. Hutchinson R. Kinkaid
President of Finque College

To Anybody:

HELP!!!

IN A FANCY
RESTAURANT

ZIT-ZIT-ZIT-ZIT-ZAT-ZAT- **SWIZAP!**

THE LIGHTER SIDE OF... STATUS

Oh, my gosh! Something new has been added! Did you have to put in a water fountain?! Now my wife is gonna get on my back to install one, too!

SEEKING

ARTIST & WRITER:
DAVE BERG

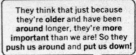

I've noticed that **most** of the girls on campus are constantly breaking their necks, trying to make "status dates" just so they can be seen in **public** with them!

I mean like dating the **Captain** of the **Football Team** . . . or the **Richest Boy** in school . . . or the **Best Looking**! I think that's silly, immature and frivolous—

—don't **you**, Professor?

How about **this**?! It's another **award** for my work with the **Boy Scouts!**

Y'know what I **just figured out?** All these years that you've been telling me you were in Scouting for the sake of "**Boyhood**" you were handing me a **big fat lie!** You've **really** been in it for only **one** reason . . . to inflate your **ego!**

You've been doing it for **prestige, status** and **awards!** All this talk about doing it for "**Boyhood**" is baloney!

I am **SO** doing it for "Boyhood"!

And I'm the "**Boy**"!!

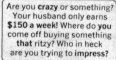

THE HEIST

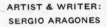

ARTIST & WRITER:
SERGIO ARAGONES

When a couple gets married, they can be sure of receiving "Greetings To The Newlyweds" cards from every conceivable source. However, despite today's frightening trend toward "All-Purpose Greeting Cards," there are still some areas and messages missing from the "Newlyweds Cards" racks. So here are:

SOME "GREETING CARDS TO THE NEWLYWEDS" WE'D LIKE TO SEE

ARTIST: BOB CLARKE
WRITER: FRANK JACOBS
IDEA: DAVID HUNTER

To Our Daughter,
The Bride —

Your wedding cost two thousand bucks,
   As well as we can judge it;
And though it was a sacrifice,
   We surely don't begrudge it;
A costly wedding's something that
   A parent understands;
We would have spent a *billion*
   Just to get you off our hands!

                Mom & Dad

To The Newlyweds—

As you cruise down the road of life
  In blissful love requited,
Remember that you're now a team—
  A happy pair united!

  In case this verse perplexes you,
    There's no need to feel troubled;
  It's just our way of saying that
    Your premiums have doubled!

ACME AUTO INSURANCE CO.

To the New Couple

Today you two appear to be
  A young, devoted duo;
But soon will come the arguments
  About the bills that you owe;
And after that the knock-down fights,
  The cursing and the shrieking;
So why not call us up right now
  While both of you are speaking!

HIGGENBOTTOM & SMEED
Divorce Lawyers

TO
THE
YOUNG
HUSBAND –

We've Pepto-Bismol by the case;
　　We've lots of Bromo fizzes;
We've Rollaids, Tums and Bisodol
　　And seltzers that are whizzes;
We've pills for cramps and stomach pains
　　Most anywhere you're looking,
So stock up now and be prepared
　　For eating your wife's cooking!

PHILO'S
PHARMACY

DEAR
YOUNG
MARRIEDS–

Your skills in self-defense may seem
  A trifle weak and spotty;
If so, it's time to take our course
  In judo and karate;
Though both of you may pray for peace
  And feel each man's your brother,
You'll need our course for all those fights
  You're having with each other!

**MIGHTY MISHKIN'S
SCHOOL OF SELF DEFENSE**

DEAR
HONEYMOONERS—

Your wedding trip is over now;
*   Your honeymoon is ended;*
We're sure you liked your stop-off here
*   And found the weather splendid;*
By now, you must be settled down;
*   Your brand-new home is started*
With all those blankets, chairs and lamps
*   You stole when you departed!*

MAGNOLIA MOTEL

CONGRATULATIONS!

Right now you're looking forward to
    Those years of joy you'll spend;
But one day when you're old and gray
    Your life on earth will end;
We'll give you an eternal bond
    That death can never sever,
Just send some cash and we'll make sure
    You're side by side forever!

CRESTVIEW CEMETERY
Lay-Away Plan Dept.
"Let Us Plot Your Future"

To the
Young Bride —

This greeting card, oh brand-new wife,
  To you we are directing;
Although you're only wed a month,
  Next week you are expecting;
No need to feel embarrassed that
  You're . . . er . . . well somewhat early;
Our staff's been told to just explain
  You gave birth prematurely!

OAKVIEW
MATERNITY HOSPITAL

TO THE
YOUNG HUSBAND—

This summer your young wife and you
    Will take your first vacation!
The trip that we are mapping out
    Will fill you with elation!
You'll take a jet for seven days
    In sunny Greece and Turkey;
Your wife, meanwhile, will holiday
    In mid-town Albuquerque!

AA TRAVEL BUREAU

GREETINGS!

As you begin your married life,
    You'll find out that the first years
Are filled with dreadful screaming fights;
    They're certainly the worst years;
To separate you from this fate
    Of ugliness and sorrow,
Young husband, you'll be glad to learn
    We're drafting you tomorrow!

Your Draft Board

We received innumerable comments and inquiries concerning the marvelous Origami animals made expressly for MAD's recently-concluded subscription ad series by Giuseppe Baggi. And so, in response to popular demand, Mr. Baggi returns with his unique . . .

MAD
ORIGAMI

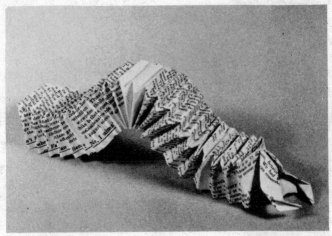

THE BOOK WORM

THE SOCIAL BUTTERFLY

ZOO
OF
CLICHÉ
CREATURES

ORIGAMI BY GIUSEPPE BAGGI

WRITER: FRANK JACOBS

THE ROAD HOG

THE BOOZE HOUNDS

THE COOL CAT

THE SPELLING BEE

THE SONG BIRD

THE CAMERA BUG

THE CARD SHARK

THE CLOTHES HORSE

THE FAST BUCK

THE WALL STREET BULLS AND BEARS

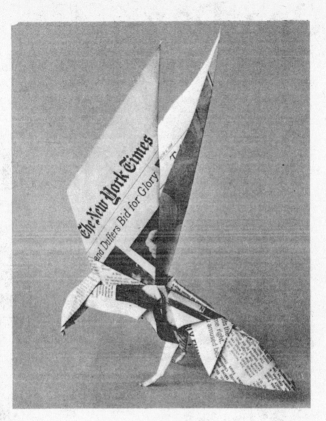

THE NEWS HAWK

One Day
In
A Hospital

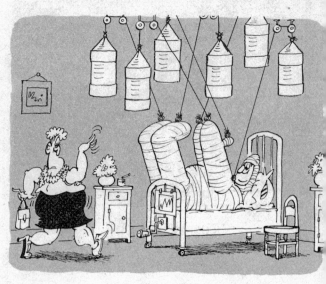

The noted scientist, Eli Mathers (Hofstra '48), once theorized: "We can learn a lot about ourselves from other forms of life, and they, in turn, can learn a lot about themselves from us!" Eli's father, Professor

Leonard Mathers (UCLA '21), once said this about his son's theory: "Eli's got a big mouth! Don't pay him no mind! Pass the salt . . ." And so, ignoring Eli Mathers' theory, we now present . . .

LOOK AT 'N WORMS 'N THINGS

Y'know those "Cartoon Sound Effects" like **"BANG!"** and **"SOCK!"** and **"SPLAT-T!"** and **"WHAM!"** that we see in our daily Comic Strips? Wouldn't it be more effective if these "Sound Effects" actually repre-

A MAD PORTFOLIO OF...

APPROPRIATE
SOUND

ARTIST: BOB CLARKE
WRITER: EARLE DOUD

sented what was taking place in the Comic Strip? To explain what we mean, here is . . .

COMIC STRIP EFFECTS

If you've seen it, you'll know exactly what we're talking about! And if you haven't seen it, rest assured that we've just saved you from

201 MIN. OF A SPACE IDIOCY

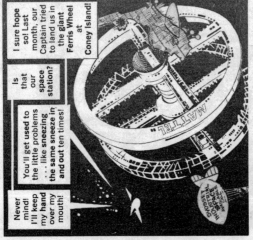

ON BOARD "MISADVENTURE I"—THE JUPITER MISSION—SEVERAL MOONS LATER

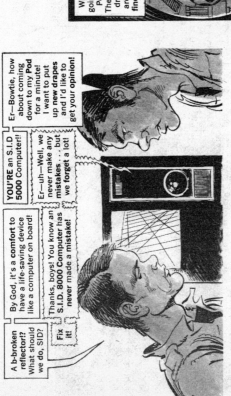

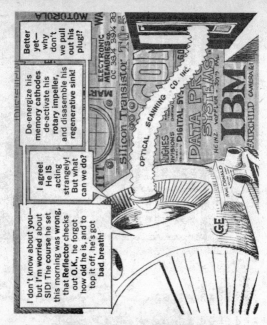

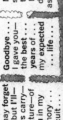

MANY MOONS LATER—OFF JUPITER

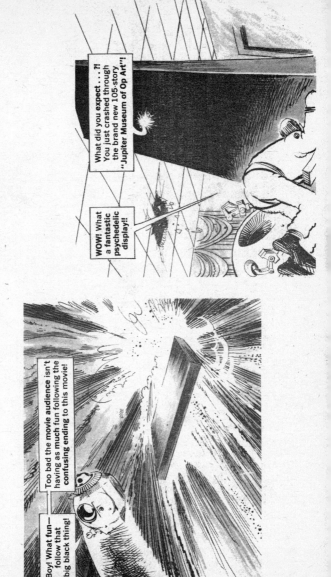

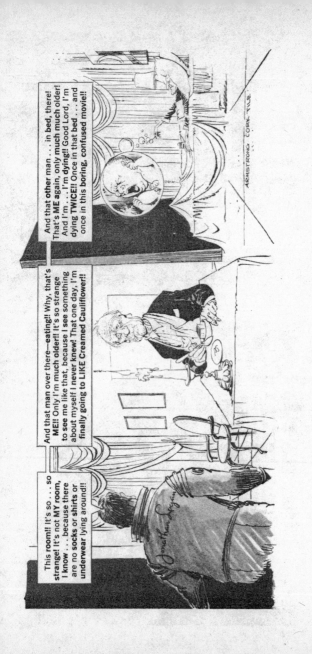

A few issues back, MAD published some samples of a little-known early 1918 comic strip from the Hamburg Post-Dispatch which presented the other side of that epic struggle of World War I ... mainly Snoopy's run-ins with The Red Baron. Now, in response to popular demand (and because the author knows we have relatives living in Germany), here are some

Further Adventures Of The Red Baron

OR "Security Ist Eine Grounded

Beaglehundt"

ARTIST: JACK RICKARD

WRITER: FRANK JACOBS

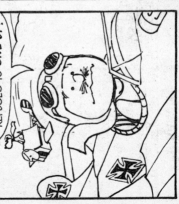

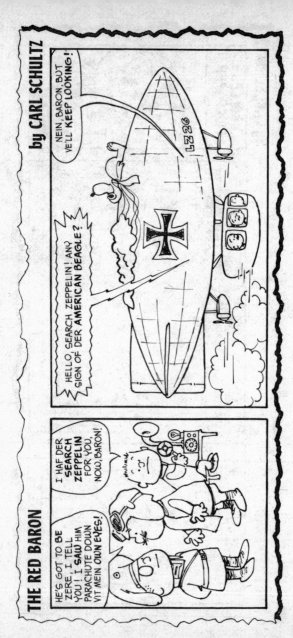

THE RED BARON
by CARL SCHULTZ
TODAY IS DER RED BARON'S BIRTHDAY!
YAH! ALL DER PILOTS ARE CHIPPING IN TO BUY HIM A GIFT!
A PRESENT ?! FOR ME...?
OPEN IT, BARON!
OPEN IT!
I FAIL TO SEE VOT IS SO FUNNY!!

IN AN ITALIAN RESTAURANT

THE ANATOMY OF A MOVIE AD CAMPAIGN

ARTIST: BOB CLARKE

WRITER: DICK DE BARTOLO

On January First, Nineteen Hundred and Seventy,
Reserved Seat Tickets will go on sale for...

"Whispering Branches"

THE GREATEST LOVE STORY EVER TOLD
A TENDER AND TOUCHING FILM OF YOUNG LOVE
THREE HOURS AND TWENTY-ONE MINUTES OF RAPTURE
A MOTION PICTURE YOU WILL TALK ABOUT FOR YEARS TO COME

OPENS JANUARY 15, 1970
at the CINEMIRACLE THEATRE

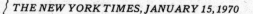

THE DAILY NEWS, January 23, 1970 ☆ ☆ ☆

COMING WEDNESDAY!

DIRECT FROM ITS RECENT GALA RESERVED SEAT ENGAGEMENT!
UNCUT! JUST THE WAY SO MANY PEOPLE SAW IT ON BROADWAY!

"Whispering Branches"

**A Hard-Hitting Modern Story Of Young Love
Designed To Shock You Out Of Your Seat!**

**3 Hours And 21 Minutes Of
Sure-Fire Entertainment!**

SEE IT AT ONE OF THESE SELECTED "HIT SHOWCASE" THEATRES

| The BEEKMAN ART | The ART EAST | The EAST ART | The ART BEEKMAN |
| The BEEKMAN EAST | The EAST BEEKMAN | The BELCH ART | The ART BURP |

✪ **NOW AT POPULAR PRICES!!** ✪

FIRST-RUN NEIGHBORHOOD

PLAYHOUSE THEATER
presents

DIRECT FROM ITS GALA RESERVED SEAT ENGAGEMENT ON BROADWAY
AND ITS RECORD-BREAKING RUN AT "HIT SHOWCASE THEATRES"!

"Whispering Branches"

A HARD-HITTING STORY OF ILLICIT YOUNG LOVE
THAT WILL BLAST YOU RIGHT OUT OF YOUR SEAT!

DON'T REVEAL THE SHOCKING CONTENTS
OF THIS PICTURE TO YOUR FRIENDS!

2 HOURS & 6 MINUTES OF SOCK!

RECOMMENDED FOR ADULTS ONLY

☆ **STARTS TODAY FOR ONE WEEK ONLY!** ☆

ILLVILLE WEEKLY STAR   February 5, 1970

NOW PLAYING!!
"I Was A Teenage Motorcycle Gang"
plus
"Whispering Branches"

R.K.O. Styx Theatre   Main Street

ILLVILLE WEEKLY STAR   February 12, 1970

TRIPLE-THREAT DRIVE-IN

"HOME OF THE HITS"   "ALWAYS A GOOD SHOW"

Route 189 at the Traffic Circle

PRESENTS

AN ALL-COLOR, ALL SPECTACULAR GALA PROGRAM

Cecil B. DeMille's "THE TEN COMMANDMENTS'

A N D

"BEN HUR" with Charlton Heston

A N D

"CLEOPATRA" with Liz and Dick

PLUS

20 Color Cartoons and 6 Travelogues

AND AS AN EXTRA ADDED ATTRACTION

"Whispering Branches"

TV GUIDE

Monday   March 9, 1970

11:30 **2** THE LATE SHOW—MOVIE

COLOR "Whispering Branches" 1969
A young man and a young woman find
love. (75 min.)

TV GUIDE

Wednesday   May 13, 1970

3:15 AM **7** INSOMNIAC THEATRE

COLOR "Whispering Branches" 1969
61 minutes of film fare designed to
have you asleep in no time.

Folks, during this brief shower, while
the game's been halted, let's watch
some of today's stand-by film feature
. . . **"Whispering Branches"** . . .

THE LIGHTER

AMUSE

ARTIST & WRITER: DAVE BE

SIDE OF...

MENT PARKS

No kiddin'?! Somehow, I can't **picture** her as the **brave** type!

You mean Nancy **didn't scream** at all?!

That's **right!** Mainly because she **fainted!!**

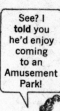

4 POSES 25¢

Yecch! These are **awful**! That's **not** me! Look at that **ugly nose** and that **silly grin**! That's **not** me! And look at that **chin**, and those **ears** sticking out, and that **messy hair**! That's **not** me!

Le'me see those pictures . . .

Are you **crazy**?! These pictures are **great**! They make you look like a **beautiful, intelligent, desirable, sexy young chick**!

That's ME!!

On

A

Saturday

Afternoon

THWIP

A MAD LOOK AT DOGS

ARTIST & WRITER: SERGIO ARAGONES

OWNERS
OF
UNLEASHED
DOGS
WILL BE
FINED!

There has been a lot of talk lately about the serious problem of our American cities. Unfortunately, up to now, no one has done an "in-depth" study of the situation. And we're certainly not going to be the first! So, in keeping with the superficial nature of these investigations, we now present a . . .

MAD GRAY PAPER*

"The State of Our Cities"

*THIS STARTED OUT AS A "MAD WHITE PAPER"—BUT WE LEFT IT ON THE WINDOWSILL OVERNIGHT!

Hello, this is Harry Reasonable with a "MAD Gray Paper" on "The Problems Facing America's Cities Today". Let's start by examining one of the biggest and perhaps the most important problem of all . . . "HOUSING" . . .

Houses like these are a blight on the modern city. As "Construction Foreman," I imagine you're anxious to start knocking them down!

Knock them **down?!** Why should I be anxious to do **THAT?**

So you can put up **NEW** houses!

But these **ARE** new houses!

Oh.

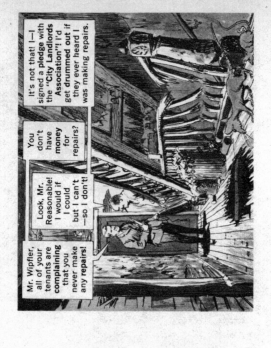

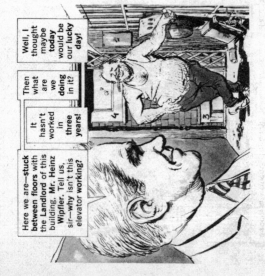

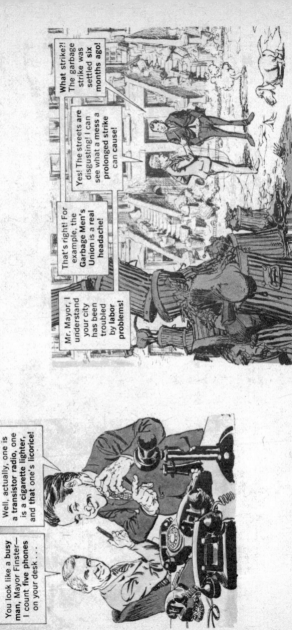